OUR FESTIVALS
Story Work Book

JET Publishing House

INDIA USA

TOWARDS EXCELLENCE

P
R
A
J
N
A

Title	**OUR FESTIVALS**
Subtitle	Story Work Book
Copyright	Jeeyar Educational Trust
First Edition	2012
Contributor	His Holiness Chinna Jeeyar Swamiji

CONTACT US:

INDIA	**UNITED STATES**
JIVA Sriramanagaram, Shamshabad, R.R. Dist. Andhra Pradesh - 509 325 Phone: 95535 49971, 95535 499	JETUSA Inc. Jeeyar Asram, 222, Dey Road, CRANBURY, NJ 08512, USA Phone:609-297-8797

Website: www.prajna4me.org   **Email:** prajna@jetusa.org

Dear friends !

On this Earth there are many countries where the ancient traditions are followed in different ways. Each country has its own way of following those traditions. But, each one of those traditions is meant for some sort of education to their masses. Each one of those customs has a wonderful value behind it. In the name of globalization, now a days, many customs or the value based practices are being discouraged and also eradicated under the mask of superstitions.

Those customs which were in use, were probably established basing upon the environmental condition or geographical condition or the background of the lineages. Though few things are changing here and there, but the fundamental truths, as a whole, like respecting the father, mother, teacher, elders and showing concern for The Nature, protecting the Earth, cattle and showing our gratitude for the sources from where we are receiving some sort of help, won't change. So irrespective of, what continent we belong to, it is the primary duty of every one to learn the basic things of benevolence which are universally practiced. It is the duty of the learned to identify such practices and put them in order, teach them to the generations so that they build the future world.

JET is offering its part of service in this context, by promoting classes called "Prajna", targeting kids and children. Children are our future world. If they learn good things, definitely they make the future brighter. So, Prajna is coming up with a few modules for children.

The first module is aimed at understanding the daily activities and also annual festivities. Here is a text book followed by an activity book. We invite all the interested volunteers to learn the content and become good guides for children. For such interested guides, -here is a handy guide provided! These modules lead children step by step "**Towards excellence**". We appreciate feedback from the well wishers for effective improvement.

We offer our Mangalasasanams to all those who made good efforts in laying the steps, building these modules and to those who use them.

INTRODUCTION

JETUSA is conducting Prajna classes for the last five years all over America . In these classes, children and adults learn vedic tradition and culture as passed on to us by our great sages. His Holiness Sri Tridandi Chinna Srimannarayana Ramanuja Jeeyar Swamiji from India directs the worldwide program to bring awareness of values and morals back into the society, emphasizing practice of vedic tradition in this scientific age.

About Sri Swamiji

His Holiness Sri Chinna Jeeyar Swamiji is a prodigious, young acharya and a noble saint who mastered different branches of the Vedic Literature, Sanathana Dharma and several scriptures. Sri Swamiji started Jeeyar Educational Trust (JET), an educational, social and charitable organization with Vedic university, affiliated colleges and residential schools such as schools for the blind, schools for tribals, dispensing holistic education and extending a helping hand to the needy ones. Please visit http://www.chinnajeeyar.org for more details.

What is Prajna?

Prajna means the ability to translate good knowledge into action. One who can properly implement his learning into practice is called Prajnaavaan or praajna.

Why Prajna ?

Vedic knowledge and culture so preciously preserved for millions of years is being lost in the modern era. We are forgetting our customs, traditions, and their importance. As a result, there is confusion in the society, leading to unrest, lack of confidence and rise of immoral behavior.

We often tend to disown and distance from our glorious past due to ignorance and misinformation. Sri Swamiji has taken up the task of informing and educating us so that we will be able to lead our lives in a fruitful way.

What are the offerings ?

Children 5 years and above learn

- Basics of our tradition
- Familiarity with vocabulary
- Introduction to vedic literature
- Stories from our history
- Biographies of great people
- Slokas, prayers and bhajans
- Virtues and values
- Festivals and community functions for families.
- Telugu language (optional)

1.Vighna Niva:rana Chathurthi

I. **Answer the following questions:**

1. In English, what is Vighna Niva:rana Chathurthi called as?

2. What help do we need to complete any activity successfully?

3. On Vighna Niva:rana Chathurthi, what do we pray for?

4. What did Pa:rvathi use, to make the doll in the form of a little boy?

5. When is Vighna Niva:rana chathurthi celebrated on?

6. Because of his elephant head, what is Gane:sa known as?

7. Who did Gaja:nana become the leader of ?

8. Gaja:nana used one of his tusks in a war; What did he hence became known as?

9. What is Gane:sa's vehicle?

10. What is the merging of clay idols of Gane:sa, in water called ?

11. Who is the alter-ego of Lord Vishnu?

12. What is the unique honor given to Vishvakse:na?

13. What are the varieties of battalions Vishvakse:na has?

14. What are two tusked Gaja:nana:s called ?

15. What is the Sanskrit word for mouth?

16. The slo:ka "sukla:mbara dharam" is a prayer on whom?

17. Who is the consort of Lord Vishvakse:na?

18. Name the precious gem given to Sathra:jith.

19. How much gold did the Syamanthakamani give in a day?

20. Who is the daughter of Ja:mbava:n?

21. Who is the daughter of Sathra:jith?

22. Who did Krushna previously incarnate as?

23. Vishwakse:na looks similar to whom?

I. Fill in the blanks:

1. For the removal of obstacles, devotees of Lord Vishnu pray to
   _____

2. For the removal of obstacles, devotees of Lord Siva pray to
   _____

3. _____ was cursed by Pa:rvathi.

4. Vighna niva:rana Chathurthi is celebrated in _____ number of days.

5. Two tusked Gaja:nana:s are called _____

II. Match the following:

a. Vighna niva:rana Chathurthi   Mo:daka:s

b. Brother of Sathra:jith   fourth day of the Bha:drapada month

c. Vishvakse:na likes   Skanda

d. Gane:sa likes   Prase:na

e. Leader of Bhu:tha gana:s   appams

f. Daughter of Sathra:jith   Lord Vishnu

g. Ja:mabava:n fought with Krushna for 28 days

h. Vishwakse:na looks similar to   Sathyabha:ma

i. Brother of Gane:sa   Gaja:nana

III. Synonyms

Gane:sa =

Vishwakse:na =

IV. Think:

What similarity can you find in rain and troubles? Think!

V. Learn Sanskrit

Nirma:lya =

Se:sha prasa:dam =

Vakthra =

VI. Learn More:

a. Doing parikrama, once around your parents is equal to going round the earth.

b. With the blessings of your parents, you can achieve the highest post / rank in your job/studies. You will always be successful.

c. Everyone faces troubles in life. You must be strong and face them boldly. Victory is yours.

d. Don't be too crazy and become greedy to earn more and more money. You will lose your peace of mind.

e. Use your thinking capabilities too, instead of depending on your physical strength alone. Most of the times it is the shortcut for success.

f. Don't make fun of people when they are in trouble. Instead help them.

g. Divine strength always helps us. Pray to God and do your duty.

h. Our Ve:dic culture pays respect to all beings - from rats to elephants. It teaches us to serve all beings. Hence the slogan - "Serve all beings as service to God"

VII. Project:

Construct a Pa:lavelli as shown in the picture below

VIII. Research:

Our scriptures recommend us not to sleep on the north- side. Do you know why?

IX. Distinguish the features of Gaja:nana and Gane:sa

X.   Word Search

APPAM, CHATURTHI, GAJANANA, GANESA, SIVA, SUTHRAVATHI, TUSK, VAKTHRA,
VISHNU, VISHVAKSENA

```
A  I  W  V  P  M  A  U  Q  O  J  A  H  T  K
P  K  H  N  I  R  F  U  D  G  A  N  E  S  A
P  Y  J  T  H  S  F  H  L  L  S  A  Q  K  H
A  H  Z  T  R  T  H  W  Q  U  L  N  I  V  Y
M  G  K  Z  U  U  U  N  T  V  R  A  V  C  F
S  A  J  S  Y  Q  T  H  U  Q  G  J  N  T  G
V  T  K  E  G  H  R  A  F  L  Y  A  G  P  O
Y  M  P  W  K  A  G  T  H  Z  I  G  O  X  T
P  N  Z  T  V  G  U  U  T  C  E  N  K  X  X
Y  N  O  A  P  I  C  X  O  T  L  J  O  K  K
Y  Z  T  A  N  E  S  K  A  V  H  S  I  V  H
R  H  P  P  T  R  P  A  R  K  D  J  R  Q  G
I  Z  N  L  Z  M  C  V  Q  E  G  U  S  P  F
H  I  L  X  A  Z  J  X  W  F  Q  I  Y  Z  N
A  V  I  S  G  U  Y  E  Y  X  C  R  A  H  P
```

2.Vijayadasami

I.   **Answer the following questions:**

1)   What is the grand finale day of Sarannavara:thri called?

2)   In which month is Dasara celebrated?

3)   For how many days is Dasara celebrated?

4)   As recommended in Ve:da:s, which plant is worshipped on Vijayadasami?

5)   Who chanted Sami: prayers, the first time on Vijayadasami?

6)   Which epic is chanted during Dasara?

7)   Who hid their weapons on Sami: tree during their ajna:thava:sa?

8)   Which Goddess is represented by Sami: tree?

9)   On which day, is Lord Venkate:swara' s birthday celebrated ?

10)   What is the birth star of Lord Venkate:swara?

11) What are the other names of Dasara?

12) For what purpose is Vijaya Dasami celebrated?

13) Sami: tree represents whom?

14) What do we achieve when we start any work on Vijayadasami?

15) Among all trees, what is Sami: tree considered as?

16) How many Goddesses are worshipped during Dasara?

17) In which ruthu is Vijayadasami celebrated?

18) What types of tools and instruments can you worship on Vijayadasami?

19) How do we celebrate the ninth day of this festival?

20) Which tree did Lord Venkate:swara worship?

II. Unscramble the words. Discover the hidden message by placing the numbered letters in the message below.

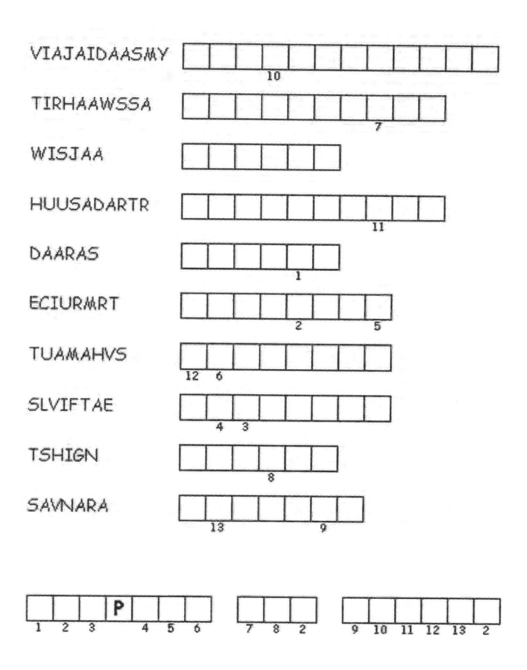

VIAJAIDAASMY — [ ][ ][ ][ ][ ][ ][ ][ ][ ][ ][ ]
₁₀

TIRHAAWSSA — [ ][ ][ ][ ][ ][ ][ ][ ][ ]
₇

WISJAA — [ ][ ][ ][ ][ ][ ]

HUUSADARTR — [ ][ ][ ][ ][ ][ ][ ][ ][ ][ ]
₁₁

DAARAS — [ ][ ][ ][ ][ ][ ]
₁

ECIURMRT — [ ][ ][ ][ ][ ][ ][ ][ ]
₂ ₅

TUAMAHVS — [ ][ ][ ][ ][ ][ ][ ][ ]
₁₂ ₆

SLVIFTAE — [ ][ ][ ][ ][ ][ ][ ][ ]
₄ ₃

TSHIGN — [ ][ ][ ][ ][ ][ ]
₈

SAVNARA — [ ][ ][ ][ ][ ][ ][ ]
₁₃ ₉

[ ][ ][ ][P][ ][ ][ ]   [ ][ ][ ]   [ ][ ][ ][ ][ ][ ]
1 2 3   4 5 6   7 8 2   9 10 11 12 13 2

III. Learn More

1. In our Ve:dic tradition. God is worshipped as several forms of nature.

2. We celebrate festivals only on the day they should be celebrated, and not during weekends that follow them because the prescribed days are auspicious according to that particular time and season.

3. We should show respect to nature, because without nature we cannot live.

4. Bommala koluvu – is keeping rows of toys in an altar for nine days, with several themes during Dasara.De:vi: navara:thri is another name for Dasara. De:vi means Goddess Lakshmi. During the nine nights, we worship Her in several forms.

IV. Find the differences in the pictures below

V.   Research

1.   Collect the various pictures for Bommala koluvu in an album form.

2.   Search the botanical name of Sami: and also its significance.

3.   Find the Recipe for the Preparation of Kajjika:yas - a delicious Indian, stuffed sweet.

VII.   Learn more

1.   The Eight forms of Maha:lakshmi are –

A:di Lakshmi

Dha:nya Lakshmi

Dhairya Lakshmi

Gaja Lakshmi

Santha:na Lakshmi

Vijaya Lakshmi

Vidya Lakshmi

Dhana Lakshmi.

2.   Here are a few more trees which represent the God or Goddess

a.   Neem - Lakshmi

b.   Aswaththam - Vishnu

c.   Usiri Amla - Vishnu

d.   Thulasi (white) – Lakshmi

e.   Black Tulasi – Vishnu

f.   Jammi – Fire God

3.   Many Indian customs, practised for centuries are meant to save the Earth and these are eco- friendly. Some of them are:

a)   Usage of jute bags, for bringing groceries and vegetables.

b)   Keeping a garden of fruits, vegetables and flowers around one's house.

c)   Usage of organic fertilizers like cow manure, etc.

d)   Breeding cattle which graze on grass alone; No hormonal injections given to them.

VII. **Can you name the Lakshmi De:vis in the picture below:**

VIII. **Match the following:**

During navara:thri , we worship:

a.	Mu:la star	Vijaya Lakshmi,
b.	Ashtami	A:yudha:s
c.	Navami	Dhairya Lakshmi
d.	Dasami	Vidya Lakshmi

IX. List and draw the various items or instruments that you pray to, on Maharnavami at your homes.

X. Coloring Corner:

XI. **Project: Draw a Sami: tree around Goddess Maha:lakshmi; show all branches of the tree tied with Sami: prayer slips**

3.Di:pa:vali

I. Answer the following questions:

1. Why do we celebrate Di:pa:vali?

2. How do we celebrate Di:pa:vali?

3. Who is the hero in the story of Di:pa:vali?

4. What is unique in the celebration of Di:pa:vali?

5. Who is the villain in the story?

6. How was Naraka:sura killed?

7. Who killed Naraka:sura?

8. Why do you say Naraka: was a villain?

9. List a few fireworks.

10. What are the precautions taken while handling fireworks?

11. Why do you light lamps on Di:pa:vali?

II. Projects :

1. Can you draw a picture of Naraka: - the demon?

2. How many Di:pa:vali sweets can you eat in 2 minutes? Count them and tell us in the class.

3. Make a clay lamp and decorate it.

III. Learn More

1. HH Sri Chinnajeeyar Swamiji was born on the day of Di:pa:vali.

2. Sathyabha:ma was an "amsa" of Bhu:De:vi and her son was Naraka:.

3. Lord Krushna started killing demons when he was 2 days old!

4. Lord Krushna protected 16000 ladie1321s.

5. Lord Krushna is called Murahari, because he killed Mura:sura.

6. Lord Krushna's vehicle - Garuda is an Eagle, the king of birds.

7. Lord Vishnu rests on a serpent called A:dise:sha who has one thousand heads.

8. Goddess Maha: Lakshmi was born from the milk-ocean.

9. Goddess Maha: Lakshmi is the spouse of Lord Vishnu

10. Sudarsana chakra is used for the protection of Vishnu's devotees.

IV. Word Search

```
P   R   A   G   J   Y   S   O   T   A   A   H   I   S   N

A   H   A   M   A   A   V   I   Q   M   D   F   U   F   A

V   R   B   C   S   Q   P   X   K   A   U   R   P   Q   R

J   D   U   T   B   L   S   O   R   H   R   F   D   H   A

A   A   H   S   M   Q   F   H   U   B   A   P   L   L   K

Y   R   L   D   A   U   X   I   S   A   G   Y   T   V   A

A   B   E   A   Y   R   E   U   H   Y   D   B   F   V   T

B   Q   N   F   D   K   U   Q   N   H   M   P   O   L   J

D   S   A   Q   U   K   W   M   A   T   A   V   Z   A   V

T   J   U   H   R   J   T   C   F   A   N   T   D   K   C

P   V   W   N   G   H   C   D   G   S   L   X   H   T   T

Y   L   O   M   A   E   K   W   L   H   A   L   I   N   A

V   W   U   G   M   A   Y   Q   S   Z   P   N   M   W   J

Y   D   H   G   G   R   M   N   A   V   G   A   C   W   P

T   Z   F   A   J   R   Q   H   C   A   C   Z   C   U   F
```

AGNI	KRUSHNA
ANILA	MURASURA
DURGAM	NARAKA
GARUDA	SASTHRA
JALA	SATHYABHAMA

V. Crossword Puzzle

Across

1 This gives light

8 Hero of Go:kulam

6 Festival of lights

Down

2.   Wife of Krushna

5.   They are also called fire-crackers

7.   One type of firework

3.   King of Gods

Learn Sanskrit:

Lamp	Di:pam
Fire	Agni
Wheel	Chakram
Water-God	Varuna
Village	Puram
Mace	Gadha
New moon day	Ama:va:sya

Research

Di:pa:vali is celebrated in the month of Ka:rthika. In which month were you born according to the Ve:dic calendar? Find out at least two people you know, who were born in the same month.

VI. Match the following with pictures

1. Lamp

2. Bhuchakra

3. Rockets

4. Naraka:sura

5. Vara:ha

6. Garland

7. Eagle

8. Divine Discus

9. Sword

10. Divine Conch

VII. Choose the correct answer

1. Di:pa:vali is the festival of

a) Lamps   b) Colors   c) Electricity   d) Sweet

2. The word Di:pa:vali means

a) An array of lamps b) A row of sweets

c) An array of crackers d) An array of flowers

3. On Di:pa:vali, people worship

a) The Goddess of wealth - Lakshmi b) The Goddess of education – Saraswathi

c) Goddess Durga d) Goddess Pa:rvathi

4. Di:pa:vali is celebrated in the Telugu month of

a) A:shwiyuja   b) Ka:rthika c) Ma:rgasirha d) Chaithra

5. Di:pa:vali is celebrated on the day of _____

a) New moon b) Full moon c) Chathurdasi d) Thrayo:dasi

6. Di:pa:vali was started to celebrate the victory of

a) Lord Ra:ma b) Lord Vishnu c) Lord Krushna d) Lord Vara:ha

7. The original name of Naraka:sura was

a) Bhanu b) Bhima c) Bhauma d) Buddha

8. Naraka:sura was the son of

a) Lord Vara:ha and Bhu:De:vi b) Lord Vishnu and Sri:De:vi

c)Lord Ra:ma and Sitha: De:vi d) Lord Krushna and Satyabhama

9. Naraka: was killed by

a) Satyabhama's arrow b)Krushna's sudarsana

c) Ra:ma's arrow d)Balara:ma's mace

IX. Fill up the blanks

1. If darkness denotes ignorance/sorrow, bright light denotes _____.

2. On Di:pa:vali, people in India light not only electric lamps but also _____ lamps with wick and oil.

3. The name of Naraka:'s capital city was _____.

4. Bhu:De:vi means the Mother -_____

X. Mark True or False against each statement:

1. Naraka was killed by Sathyabha:ma.

2. Krushna's divine flight is Garuda.

3. Krushna kidnapped 16,000 princesses from Naraka.

4. On the day of Di:pa:vali, people worship Goddess Lakshmi at sunset and offer sweets.

5. The day after Di:pa:vali is known as Naraka Chathurdasi.

XI. Find at least 20 differences

XII. Cryptogram

A	B	C	D	E	F	G	H	I	J	K	L	M	N	O	P	Q	R	S	T	U	V	W	X	Y	Z
13	16	9	15	17	8	5	22	23	19	14	1	20	26	11	7	2	6	12	24	25	18	4	10	3	21

— —   — — — — —   — —   — — — — —
13 26   13 6 6 13 3   11 8   1 13 20 7 12

XIII. Color the lamp

4.Dhanurma:sam

I) **Fill up the blanks:**

1) A:lwa:r means_____.

2) A:nda:l lived in _____.

3) Go:da married _____.

4) The two scriptures composed by Go:da are_____and

_____.

5) "Go:da" means_____.

6) The day Go:da married Rangana:tha is celebrated as _____.

7) "A:nda:l" means _____.

8) Go:da De:vi's thirty songs are called _____.

9) The parrot in Go:da De:vi's hand represents _____.

10) Go:da de:vi performed Dhanurma:sa vratham in the month of _____.

II) Give one word answers to the following questions:

a) Where did Vishnu Chittha find Go:da?

b) What did Vishnu Chittha offer to the Lord every day?

c) Whose stories was Go:da de:vi fascinated to?

d) What did Vishnu Chittha find in the garland one day?

e) What garlands did Vishnu Chittha prepare for God?

f) What vratham did Go:da de:vi perform?

g) How many songs did Go:da de:vi sing in Thiruppa:vai?

h) How many songs are there in Na:chhiya:r Thirumo:zhi?

i) What happened to Go:da de:vi when she entered the sanctum in Sri:rangam?

j) What festival is celebrated on the day after Bho:gi?

III) Match the following words with corresponding pictures.

1. Dwa:parayuga

2. A:nda:l rangammannar

3. Thiruppa:vai

4. A:muktha ma:lyada

5. Bho:gi

6. Vishnu chittha

7. Go:da

8. Vatapathrasa:yi

9. Sri:rangam

10. Sankra:nthi

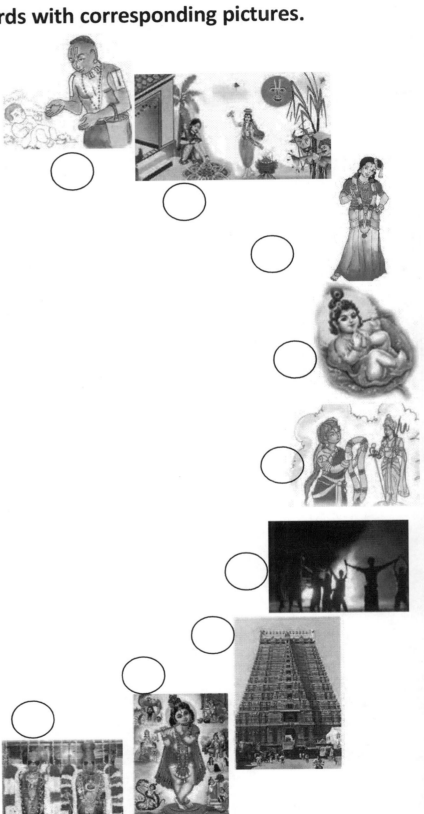

IV) Synonyms

1) Go:da, A:nda:l, A:mukthama:lyada, Su:dikoduttha na:chchiya:r, pa:dikoduttha na:chchiya:r

2) Vishnuchittha, Periya:lwa:r, Bhattana:thulu.

V) Learn More

a) Love God whole heartedly; He fulfills all your wishes.

b) Archa: - deity form, is God Himself.

c) God is only One, but in several forms.

d) In whatever language you speak to Him in, He understands you.

e) Traditionally we Ve:dics use Sanskrit language, to pray to the Lord.

f) God loves sincere, honest people; He always protects them.

g) God lives in pure hearts.

h) The songs sung by A:lwa:rs are called Divya prabandham.

VI True or False

1. A:nda:l was married to Lord Rangana:tha.

2. Thiruppa:vai consists of 40 verses.

3. Dhanurma:sam is celebrated in the months of August and September.

4. Go:da:de:vi was found near a temple.

VII) Word Search

Tulalsi, Narayana, Krushna, Dhanurmasam, Rangamannar, Periyalwar, Andal, Thiruppavai, Bhogi.

```
Y   D   P   T   Q   M   L   V   L   Z   M   A

T   E   E   O   I   J   Z   A   L   A   V   N

K   H   R   R   F   S   D   G   S   F   I   H

K   O   I   Z   I   N   A   A   P   N   O   S

I   U   Y   R   A   W   M   L   G   L   H   U

A   Y   A   Y   U   R   E   M   U   Q   B   R

Q   C   L   Y   U   P   Y   W   Y   T   A   K

E   A   W   N   D   S   P   B  -H   O   G   I

G   R   A   N   G   A   M   A   N   N   A   R

K   H   R   F   Z   K   F   H   V   N   R   A

D   A   N   A   Y   A   R   A   N   A   C   O

I   A   S   E   D   W   N   A   Q   I   I   P
```

VIII) Crossword Puzzle:

Across

1. Deity of Sri:rangam

4. A song sung by Go:da

6. Yuga in which Krushna was born

9. Father of Go:da•

Down

2. 30 songs of Go:da

3. Language in which A:nda:l sang

5. Another name of Go:da

7. A leaf on which baby Krushna lays

8. Sacred plant

10. Gaurdian of God

IX) Research

a) Collect the names and pictures of 5 ancient temples.

b) How many A:lwa:rs are there? Name at least three of them.

c) Do we have a lady A:lwa:r? If so, who is she?

d) Can you name an A:lwa:r who had the complexion of Sri Krushna.

e) Name different vrathams.

f) Below is a picture of Satta:ri you see in the temple. This represents an A:lwa:r. Who is it?

X) Picture

a) Color the picture of Go:da

b)   Sankra:nthi is a festival of prosperity and reverence to nature. Color the picture.

XI) Project

Color and Decorate Go:da De:vi with the below ornaments looking in to the model gi

1. Garland
2. Chains
3. Parrot
4. Crown
5. Bottu

6. Nose ring
7. Earrings
8. Waist belt
9. Bangles

XII) Can you find – a peacock, lotus, peacock feather, flute, garland, hill, tree and ladies with fruits in this picture?

XIII. Spot at least 8 differences:

5. UGA:DI

I) **Answer the following questions:**

1. What is the name of the Telugu New year?

2. What is the special dish you eat on Uga:di?

3. According to which calendar do we celebrate Uga:di?

4. In which Ruthu do we celebrate Uga:di?

5. Gri:shma Ruthu comes after Vasantha Ruthu, true or false?

6. To whom did Bramha give the archa: form of the Lord?

7. Bramha appeared from which flower?

8. On which river bank was Lord Rangana:tha installed eventually?

9. Name three activities you do on Uga:di.

10. Which archa vigraha was given to Lord Bramha?

11. What is the difference between bath and Abhyangana sna:nam?

12. What is a Pancha:ngam?

13. What is Pancha:nga sravanam?

14. Use Pancha:ngam and tell how many birth stars are there.

15. Do you know how to make Nimbakusuma Bhakshanam (uga:di pacchadi)?

16. What is creation called in Sanskrit?

17. What is a lunar calendar?

18. What is a solar calendar?

19. In general, which calendar does your family follow?

20. How many heads does Lord Bramha have?

II. Fill in the blanks:

1. According to Ve:dic system, a new time period starts on——————.

2. Yuga means ———————————; A:di means——————

   ——————.

3. On Uga:di, we celebrate the birth day of Lord——————————.

4. Nimbakusumam means————————————————.

5. —————————— forecast the astrological influences depending on the Pancha:ngam.

III) True or False:

1. Abhyangana sna:nam means a special bath with oil massage, herbal powder and Rita extract, soap and shampoo.

2. Pancha:ngam means seven aspects about time.

3. Uga:di comes on the last day of chaithra ma:sa.

4. Nimbakusuma bhakshanam denotes the mixture of all experiences in life.

IV) Research:

1. One day of Bramha is equal to _____years for us.

2. Bramha's current age is 51 years. Can you guess how many years it is, in our time line?

3. Do you know how many birth stars are there?

4. What is your birth star?

5. People from 3 states – Andhra Pradesh, Maharashtra and Karnataka use the Lunar calendar and celebrate New Year on the first day of Lunar calendar. However, they have different names for the New Year. Name them.

V) Projects

1. Name the ingredients used in the Yuga:di chutney.

2. How do you make Yuga:di chutney?

3. On Yuga:di, the homes are decorated with "tho:ranam" using mango leaves. Make one using sample below:-

   a) Using green construction paper and cut 10 pieces of mango leaved shapes.

   b) Draw borders for those cut leaves.

   c) Take a string.

   d) Tie all the cut-leaves together using the string

   e) You can decorate it your door.

VI) Match the following

Day	09/10/2010
Date	Manda Va:sara
Star	A:nanda
Yo:ga	Kaulava
Karanam	Swathi

VII) Fun Activity

1. Nimba kusuma Bhakshanam

How many words can you make from this word?

1.

2.

3.

4.

5.

44

2. Spot at least 8 differences

VIII. Criss-Cross Puzzle

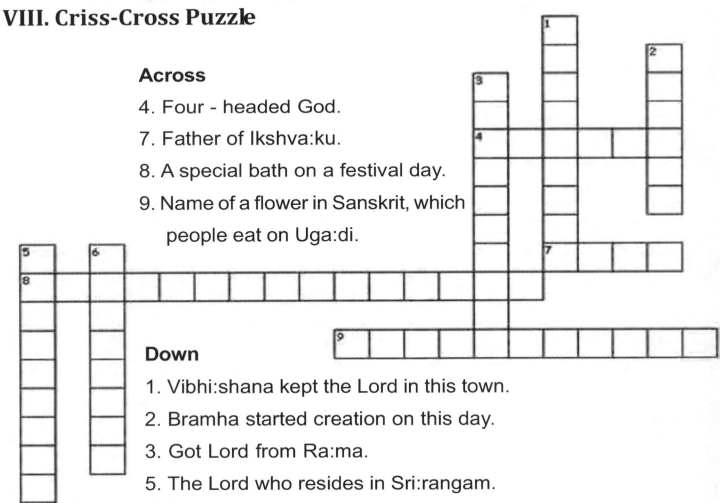

Across

4. Four - headed God.

7. Father of Ikshva:ku.

8. A special bath on a festival day.

9. Name of a flower in Sanskrit, which people eat on Uga:di.

Down

1. Vibhi:shana kept the Lord in this town.

2. Bramha started creation on this day.

3. Got Lord from Ra:ma.

5. The Lord who resides in Sri:rangam.

6. The month in which Uga:di comes.

6. Sri: Ra:ma Navami

I. Answer the following questions:

1. Who wrote Sri: Ra:ma:yanam?

2. On what day is Sri: Si:tha Ra:ma Kalya:nam performed?

3. Dasaratha is the king of which country?

4. What did Dasaratha get in Puthra Ka:me:shti?

5. Who are the parents of Lord Sri: Ra:ma?

6. What is Ra:ma's birth star?

7. In which month was Ra:ma born?

8. Who did Ra:ma marry?

9. Who is queen Kyke:yi's son?

10. Whose brothers are Lakshmana and Bharatha?

11.   Who is Ra:ma's guru?

12.   What is the ninth day from Uga:di?

13.   Who was sage Viswa:mithra to Ra:ma?

14.   How old was Ra:ma when he went to forest with Viswa:mithra?

15.   How old was Ra:ma when he was sent to forest with Si:tha?

16.   How long was Ra:ma exiled to forest?

17.   Who is the king of monkeys?

18.   Who abducted Si:tha?

19.   **What is Si:tha's place?**

20.   For how many years did Ra:ma rule Ayo:dhya?

II. True or False

1. Dasaratha did not give any pa:yasam to Sumithra.

2. Dasaratha had kids when he was 100 years old.

3. Vasishtha named all the four kids of Dasaratha.

4. Ra:ma means one who makes everyone happy.

5. Vasishtha performed Puthraka:me:shti.

III. Match the different names of Lord Sri: Ra:ma with their meanings

1. Si:tha Ra:ma   son of Kausalya

2. Ko:danda Ra:ma   son of Dasaratha

3. Ayo:dhya Ra:ma   having the bow named Ko:dhandam

4. Kausalya Ra:ma   King of Ayo:dhya

5. Dasaratha Ra:ma   married to Si:tha

IV. Match relationships to Ra:ma

Viswa:mithra   Father
Dasaratha   Brother
Kausalya   Enemy
Sumithra and Kyke:yi   Guru
Vasishtha   Friend
Bharatha   Mother
Lakshmana   }   Wife
Sathrughna
Si:tha
                          Step Mother
                          Servant

Ra:vana

Hanuma:n

Sugri:va

V. Challenge:

1. Sri: Ra:ma Navami is celebrated in Vasantha Ruthu. Name other festivals celebrated in this ruthu.

2. Sage Va:lmi:ki wrote Ra:ma:yana. Find out if he wrote Ra:mayana before or after Ra:ma was born.

3. Name other sages and their epics.

4. Prepare pa:yasam and bring it to the class.

VI. Identify or draw the following, in the map below:

1. Bridge between India and Sri: Lanka

2. Ayo:dhya

3. Mithila

VII. Choose the right answer:

1. Sri: Sita Ra:ma Kalya:nam is performed on -

    a) Krushna:shtami

    b) Maharnavami

    c) Sri: Ra:ma Navami

    d) Bhi:shma Eka:dasi

2. Dasaratha did_____before Puthraka:meshti.

    a) Narame:tha

    b)Aswame:tha

    c)Ajame:tha

    d)Aghame:tha

3. Dasaratha got a _____ in Puthra Ka:me:shti.

    a) divine milk dessert

    b) milk chocolate

    c) milk ice cream

    d) milk

4. Lord Sri: Ra:ma was the son of

    a) Kausalya and Dasaratha

    b) Kyke:yi and Dasaratha

    c) Sumithra and Dasaratha

    d) None of the above

5. Lord Vishnu was born as _____ to Dasaratha.

    a) Parasu Ra:ma

    b) Va:mana

    c) Balara:ma

    d) Sri: Ra:ma

6. Ra:ma's birth star is_____.

    a) Pushyami

    b) Pubba

    c) Punarvasu

    d) Pu:rvabha:dra

7. In which month was Ra:ma born?

    a) Vaisa:kha

    b) Aswiyuja

    c) Ka:rthika

    d) Chaithra

VIII. Find the meaning of:

1.   Ra:ma

2.   Lakshmana

3.   Bharatha

4.   Sathrughna

51

IX.   How many 'Sri: Ra:ma' s can you find in this?

```
E I R P J E E R C Q J N A H O T U M C I
O P P L S R E H W E S V C P C E N C Z T
K N H T A Q I A B F Z S F F H T U V K B
O L S M N X H Y D P N A G H S C E N T
N K E S H E S B D R P C I O D M S P S Z
S S T G O J S A D P M A F E O E M E S T
A R N D I H O E L R M D F F L I M H I E
L I I A P M E Z F A E C M L W F E R R E
V R L R J S L E R O Z N V I R R E P J H
D A V K A T U I R P V I A C E G H Y T X
U M T N R M R L F O K V Q P N S S M I G
S A V G S A H O Y W C C G H Y H U R P
A S A M A R I R S E Q F N B O M T T M P
X L H C K I S V I A A B O D L G S C E Y
N F O E J R X T K R O N B Q T W S A M R
E M G E T A N N I H S S E N N I A T E V
E J I S R M S C O N A E C O M W S M D G
G I K I S A W E O A G O D E I H E R O T
T M S W R S Z Y S S Q H U S E Q T A T I
R E V D L Q A L V I L P E S Z K L N O E
```

X. Color the picture

Learn more:

To be like...

1. Sri: Ra:ma - Make everyone happy with your good behavior and qualities.

2. Lakshmana - serve God with devotion.

3. Bharatha -take full responsibility and do your duty perfectly.

4. Sathrughna - defeat your inner enemies – anger, jealousy, etc

7. Sri: Jayanthi

I. Answer the following questions

1. Whose birthday is celebrated as Sri:Jayanthi ?

2. Who was the king of Mathura?

3. Who warned Kamsa about his death?

4. Why did Kamsa want to kill De:vaki?

5. Who was the first son of De:vaki and Vasude:va?

6. What did Lord Vishnu order Yo:gama:ya to do?

7. According to the lunar calendar, in which month was Krushna born?

8. What is the name given to the 8th day in a lunar calendar?

9. What were the previous birth names of De:vaki in which Lord Vishnu was born

9. What were the previous birth names of De:vaki in which Lord Vishnu was born as her son?

10. What river did Vasude:va cross along with Krushna to reach Nandhago:kula?

11. Who named Krushna?

12. Who was the father of De:vaki?

13. What is Krushna's birth star?

14. How many cows did Vasude:va donate, in his heart, when Krushna was born?

15. In which place did Krushna grow up?

16. Who was the grandfather of Krushna?

17. What is the name of the other wife of Vasude:va ?

18. What is Sri:jayanthi popularly known as?

19. What is similarity in "Utti" and 'Pinyata'?

20. Who is Krushna's brother?

III. Projects

1. List the various sweets and snacks prepared on Sri:jayanthi. Gather pictures and create an album.

2. Do you know the process of preparing butter and ghee in a Indian traditional way which has good cholesterol?

3. Make a cradle for Lord Sri: Krushna using popsicle sticks.

4. Find the recipe of the following snacks -

a) Ka:yam

b) Ba:dusha:

c) Murukulu

d) Navani:tham

IV. Find at least 15 differences from below pictures:

 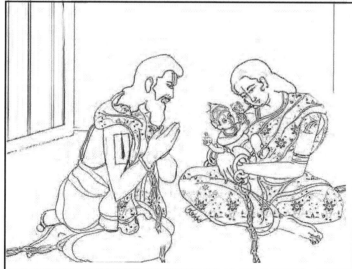

V. Research

1. What is a birth star and what is a constellation?

2. What is constellation called in Sanskrit?

3. How many stars do we have in our Ve:dic calendar?

4. How many constellations are there?

5. What is your birth star and constellation?

6. What is a paksha? Name them.

7. Krushna became the jagadguru by preaching _ _ _ to Arjuna.

VI. Synonyms

a) Krushna , Va:sude:va , Mura:ri, Naraka:nthaka, Nanda nandana

b) Bhouma, Naraka:sura,

c) Garuda, Vynathe:ya, Tharkshya, Pannagasana, Suparna, Kagendra

d) Award, reward, gift

e) Spared, freed, saved, released.

f) Krushna:shtami, Sri: Jayanthi, Janma:shtami, Kannan Thirunakshatram.

VII. Learn more

1. The wedding gifts to De:vaki from her father are:

a. 400 elephants, 15,000 horses, 1,800 chariots and

b. 200 lady servants.

2. The "A:ka:sava:ni", Asreerava:ni , the heavenly voice or radio use to warn people about forth coming events.

3. Prusni and Suthapa did penance for twelve thousand years in Swayambhu manvanthara and asked Lord Vishnu to be their son for three times.

    a.   First, Prusni and Suthapa begot a son "Prusni Garbha"
    b.   In their second life, Adithi and Kasyapa got a son "Va:mana"
    c.   In their third life De:vaki and Vasude:va got a son "Krushna"

4. Eight weapons of Yo:gama:ya are -

    1. Dhanuhu 2. Su:laha 3. Ishu 4. Charma 5. Asi, 6. Sankha

    7.   Chakra 8. Gada:

5. Let us remember the birth details of Lord Krushna through this slo:ka and learn its meaning :

Simha ma:se: asithe: pakshe: rohinya:m ashtamya:mi: thithau charamartha prada:tha:ram krushnam vande: jagadgurum.

Krishna was born on 8th day of Simhama:sa (usually in the month of August that is Sra:vanama:sa), in the Shukla paksha, when the star was Rohini. He gave quint essence of Charama Slo:ka while saying bhagavadgitha to Arujuna. Thus he became jagadguru. Let us bow at his divine lotus feet.

VIII. Color this flower to offer it to lord Krushna

light green = 1
dark green = 2
red = 3
pink = 4

orange = 5
yellow = 6
purple = 7

brown = 8
white = 9
light blue = 10

8. Guru Pu:rnima

I. Fill up the blanks:

1. Because Ve:da Vya:sa: was in Badrinath while composing the Ve:dic essence, he is also known as _____.

2. Ve:da Vya:sa's birthday is celebrated on _____ Pu:rnima.

3. Lord Vishnu's deep meditation for four months is called _____.

4. _____ is the Guru of all gurus.

5. Para:sara wrote a treasured scripture called _____

6. With the grace of God, Krushna Dwaipa:yana divided the Ve:dic mass into four parts _____, _____, _____ and _____.

7. In Sanskrit, an island is called _____

8. Ve:daVyasa's parents are _____ and _____.

9. The whole universe is always under the control of _____.

10. To support the universe, Lord Vishnu takes several incarnations called _____.

II. Match the Following:

Sra:vana Pu:rnima	education
A:sha:da Pu:rnima	Lakshmi.
Sarat Pu:rnima	Yajnas
Ka:rthi:ka Pu:rnima	Gurus
Ma:gha Pu:rnima,	Crops
Pha:lguna Pu:rnima	Bliss

III. Learn Sanskrit

1. Guru – **Gu** means ignorence, **ru** means who removes. Guru means who removes ignorence.

2. Cha:thurma:syam - "**Chathur**" means four and "**ma:sam**" means month. Chathurma:syam means four sacred months.

3. Yo:ganidra - **Yo:ga** means union and **Nidra** means coming back from regular activity.

IV. True or False

1. Ve:da Vyas wrote 20 Pura:na:s .

2. Pura:nas recorded past history.

3. Srimad Maha: Bha:ratham has 125,000 hymns.

4. Srimad Maha: Bha:ratham documented the history of Ra:ma and Si:tha.

5. Bramhasu:thras have 600 hymns.

6. The Lord starts the process of Yo:ganidra on Sra:vana Pu:rnima.

7. Bramhasu:tras are also called Ve:dantha, which contain the essence of Ve:das.

8. All the documented literature that is available today is only because of Ra:ma.

9. During Yo:ganidra Lord Vishnu focuses on finding new ways to protect the Universe.

10. During the Cha:tur ma:sam period, gurus bless the fellow citizens and their disciples with divine knowledge that they accumulated over time.

V. Learn More:

Sri: Vishnu Sahasrana:ma is a hymn with 1000 names on Lord Vishnu. Bhagawad Gi:tha is a song of 700 slo:ka:s. Both of them are from the scripture called Srimanmaha: Bha:ratham. Srimad Bha:gawath is one of the Pura:nas written by Ve:da Vya:sa.

VI. Color this picture:

VII. Spot the differences in the pictures below

9. Sra:van Pu:rnima

I.   Give One Word Answers To the Following Questions:

1.   Who created Bramha?

2.   How many heads does Lord Bramha have?

3.   What was Lord Na:ra:yana trying to teach Bramha?

4.   Who stole the Ve:da:s?

5.   Where did the demons hide the ve:da:s?

6.   Where did Bramha do the yajnam to get back Ve:dic knowledge?

7.   In what form is Lord Na:ra:yana now at Ka:nchi:puram?

8.   What did Lord Na:ra:yana bless Bramha with?

9.   In what form did the Lord go to the nether world?

10. What does "Haya" mean? Horse

11. What does "Gri:va" mean? Neck.

12. What does "Hayagri:va" mean? Horse necked God.

13. In which month did Lord Hayagri:va appear from the sacrificial fire?

14. Which day of Sra:vana is dedicated for knowledge?

15. What is the favorite dish of Lord Hayagri:va?

16. What is the tying of a wrist-band to one's brother called?

17. What is a full moon day in Sra:vana month called?

18. After performing which pu:ja, do students chant all scriptures before God?

19. What do ve:dic students perform, as a special ceremony, to pray to Lord Hayagri:va before starting new lessons?

20. What did Lord Hayagri:va do in the nether world?

21. When is Raksha bandhanam celebrated?

II. True or False

1. When Lord Hayagri:va neighed loudly in the pa:tha:lam, the demons jumped out of great joy (True/False)

2. Hayagri:va means Elephant necked God.(True/False)

3. Lord Hayagri:va is a form of all manthra:s (True/False)

4. Bramha never forgot the Ve:das when Lord gave them on Sra:vana pu:rnima day. (True/False)

5. Lord Hayagri:va appeared from the sacrificial fire on the day of Sra:vana pu:rnima (True/False)

6. Knowledge is power (True/False)

III. Fill up the blanks:

1. _____ day of _____ month is dedicated for knowledge.

2. We chant _____ everyday for acquiring intelligence, concentration, memory, oratory skills and good knowledge.

3. As a mark of oath, a _____ is tied to the hand of the person.

4. _____ is a special ceremony and a very important festival for all seekers of good knowledge.

IV.   Label the Pictures

V.   Project

Garbanzo beans is the favorite dish of Hayagri:va. Write the steps to make this prasa:d to Lord Hayagri:va

VI.   Learn More

· A student should be attentive to the teachings of guru.

· Unsought knowledge does not stay for long. So it is the duty of the student to seek knowledge from the teacher.

· If one seeks knowledge sincerely, one will remember it for a long time.

· Lord Hayagri:va is the form of Lord Na:ra:yana, to whom we should pray for good memory, concentration and oratory skills.

VII. Show what is wrong in the picture below

VIII. Spot at least 15 differences

IX. Did you know?

There are 4 Ve:das – Rig Ve:da, Yajur Ve:da, Sama Ve:da and Atharva Ve:da.

The four Ve:das have a total of 1131 branches. Out of them only 11 are now available.

Rig Ve:da describes the secrets of how to create a Universe

X. Learn Sanskrit

1. **Bramha** - one with four heads
2. **Bramha:** - bruhathi brumhayithi - one which is big and makes others big – the Supreme Lord
3. **Dharma** – Righteous practices which when followed, gives happiness in this world and in the one above.

XI. Word Search

ATHARVA; HAYAGRIVA; KANKANAM ; KNOWLEDGE; RAKSHA ; SAMA; UPAKARMA; YAJUS

```
E  B  S  E  S  F  O  Q  M  F  E  J  A  H  D
B  E  A  U  G  R  H  A  A  H  L  O  V  S  E
R  M  J  F  X  D  R  B  M  V  X  Y  I  U  J
L  A  D  U  N  H  E  P  A  C  B  T  R  B  M
Y  Z  E  N  T  Y  B  L  S  M  B  E  G  A  A
R  A  T  O  F  A  B  A  W  C  Z  G  A  V  O
Y  Y  H  Q  A  Z  V  K  M  O  E  T  Y  Y  X
W  T  K  V  B  H  A  R  J  R  N  I  A  X  H
S  S  T  U  M  N  S  Q  A  O  A  K  H  S  Y
X  Z  E  W  K  P  Y  K  F  H  Z  K  X  I  P
T  B  R  A  L  O  M  X  A  E  T  F  A  K  X
I  R  N  J  F  R  U  G  D  R  F  A  L  P  Z
L  A  O  M  E  D  U  F  F  T  C  I  Z  L  U
M  J  P  G  O  H  D  T  Y  Y  D  Z  S  K  R
T  J  S  Y  P  C  C  O  T  B  L  G  A  J  X
```

XII. Criss-Cross Puzzle

Across

3. Madhu and Kaitabha stole

5. - beans is the favorite dish of Hayagri:va

6. Hayagri:va neighed loudly in

8. Month in which Hayagri:va appeared from the yajnam

9. Madhu and Kaita:bha

10. Horse necked God

Down

1. Knowledge is

2. Varadara:ja temple is in

4. gave ve:das to Bramha

7. The God with four heads

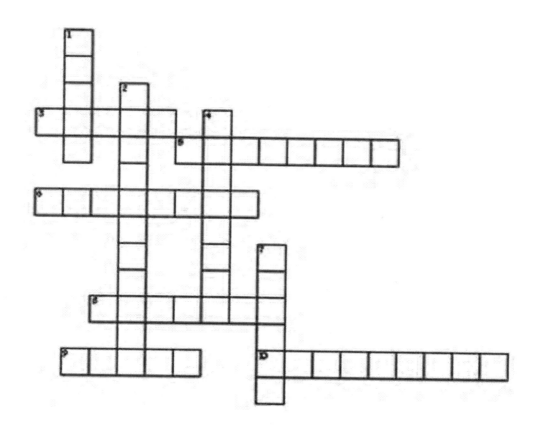

10. Little Heros

I.Answer the following questions:

1. Who is a Hero?

2. Name a few child heroes.

3. What do you have to do to be a hero?

4. How does a hero influence you?

5. Did you do any heroic activity so far?

6. Name some of the heroic actions.

7. Does a hero do heroic actions to help the society or just for his own good - for name and fame?

8. Do you think you can become a hero one day?

9. To be a hero, what are you going to do or achieve?

10. Do you think you can be a hero by controlling your sleep?

11. Who is your favorite hero from your Prajna story book?

12. Who is your favorite movie hero?

II. Project

1. Name a few heroes from different fields like firefighting, sports, army, etc. Collect their pictures.

2. Identify the heroes of India.

III. Learn More

Every hero is an ordinary boy or girl. But with determination and confidence, coupled with the quality of helping others, one can become a hero. Realize that a hero is hidden in you.

Made in the USA
Coppell, TX
26 January 2024

28208830R00042